DOCTOR WHO

DOCTOR WHO

THE SCRIPT OF THE FILM

MATTHEW JACOBS

BBC BOOKS

First published 1996 in the UK by BBC Books,
a division of BBC Worldwide Ltd, Woodlands,
80 Wood Lane, London W12 0TT
Script text copyright © BBC Worldwide and Universal Television 1996
Introduction copyright © Philip Segal 1996
Design and layout copyright © BBC Books 1996
Reprinted 1996

Original series broadcast on the BBC
Format copyright © BBC 1963
Terry Nation is the creator of the Daleks.
Doctor Who, TARDIS and the TARDIS device are all trademarks of the
British Broadcasting Company

ISBN 0 563 40499 X
Typeset by Ace Filmsetting Ltd, Frome
Printed and bound in Great Britain by Clays Ltd, St Ives plc
Cover printed by Clays Ltd, St Ives plc
Colour reproduction by Radstock Reproductions Ltd, Midsomer Norton
Colour printed by Lawrence Allen Ltd, Weston-super-Mare

INTRODUCTION

It is hard for me to believe that after so many years of watching *Doctor Who* as a fan, I am now making *Doctor Who* as a producer. I can remember when my grandfather sat me on his knee and together we watched with amazement and delight as William Hartnell first stepped across the threshold of his TARDIS into the world of a Time Lord. Now, over thirty years later, we are crossing a new threshold and once more the Doctor prepares to do battle against the nefarious Master.

When I began to discuss the idea of bringing *Doctor Who* back with the BBC, I really had no idea of the road that lay ahead for me and this project. Many years of meetings, briefings and a lot of convincing were only the first steps in bridging the creative and financial gaps between the Fox Network, Universal and the BBC. I would especially like to thank Peter Wagg for his support during this uncertain time. We were originally going to produce *Doctor Who* together, but unfortunately, after nearly four years of discussions, Peter had to move on. However, his friendship and support has stayed with the project throughout.

Once everyone agreed to move forward, we faced the difficult task of finding the right writer to realize a script that would fit the needs of the two networks, the BBC and Fox. Our search ended with Matthew Jacobs, whose close association with the Doctor was unknown to me until we met for the first time in my office in Los Angeles over a year ago. As we broke the ice and began to talk about what made the Doctor such a beloved character, Matthew explained that his father, Anthony Jacobs, was an actor in an episode of *Doctor Who* during the Hartnell years. In fact, he played Doc Holliday in *The Gunfighter*. Matthew was eight and remembers being on the set at the old Ealing Studios during filming.

Matthew's script needed to tell a story that was personal to the Doctor, dealing with his regeneration and putting him back on Earth – important because, after all, these rules would ultimately help us define the Doctor's world to the uninitiated in a much more understandable way. The concept of using the Master and none of the other monsters (apart from a brief off-camera cameo by the Daleks in the prologue) was also decided upon for this reason, as well as to make the film more feasible in terms of cost. As the creative meetings progressed, we arrived at a story that everyone signed off and Matthew went away to write it.

The script gave us many production challenges which had to be dealt with head-on if we were ever going to make *Doctor Who* become a reality. Because the story is set in San Francisco in 1999, the first thing we did was prepare a feasibility study of actually making the film there. However, once the budget and script were completely broken down and a schedule laid out, the decision was made to look for an alternative site that could double for San Francisco. Our search led us to Vancouver, BC, which has successfully doubled for San Francisco many times before. After making a complete survey of Vancouver, we began pre-production. The production team spent six weeks preparing to shoot the film – not a great deal of time for a film this size. In this very limited time, we had to hire the crew, build the sets *and* cast the film.

The casting process was very difficult because of all the different companies involved in the decision-making process. The role of the Doctor had to be approved by both the BBC and the Fox Network. All the other roles had to be approved by both Fox and Universal. My first (and only) choice for the Doctor was a man whose work I had first noticed in the film *Dealers*: Paul McGann. To me, Paul is a cross between Patrick Troughton and Tom Baker. I'm often asked which Doctor is my favourite. I always used to say, 'It's a toss-up between Patrick Troughton and Tom Baker.' However, after seeing Paul in the role, I now answer, 'Paul McGann.'

What follows is the complete and final shooting script of the Doctor's latest adventure in time and space. It seems like I have travelled down a very long road to finally see my dream of being the one to bring *Doctor Who* back to our screens become a reality. This project was a labour of love and one which I would gladly perform again.

Finally, my thanks go to the following people: Alex Beaton, Tony Greenwood, Geoff Sax, Peter Wagg, Trevor Walton, Peter Ware, Jo Wright and Alan Yentob.

And to my grandfather, the man who introduced me to *Doctor Who*.

Philip Segal
Executive Producer

This official script book contains the finalized script used throughout filming. However, there may well have been changes during the film-editing process so parts of this script may differ from what appears on the screen.

CAST

The Doctor .... Paul McGann

The Old Doctor .... Sylvester McCoy

The Master/Bruce .... Eric Roberts

Dr Grace Holloway .... Daphne Ashbrook

Chang Lee .... Yee Jee Tso

The Old Master .... Gordon Tipple

Curtis .... Dolores Drake

Wheeler .... Catherine Lough

Salinger .... John Novak

Dr Swift .... Michael David Simms

Miranda .... Eliza Roberts

Pete .... William Sasso

Ted .... Joel Wirkkunen

Anchorwoman .... Mi-Jung Lee

Co-Anchor .... Joanna Piros

CHP Cop .... Bill Croft

Security Man .... Dee Jay Jackson

Professor Wagg .... Dave Hurtubise

Gareth .... Jeremy Radick

PRODUCTION CREDITS

Executive Producers .... Alex Beaton

.... Philip Segal

Exec. Producer for the BBC .... Jo Wright

Producer .... Peter Ware

Director .... Geoffrey Sax

Co–Producer .... Matthew Jacobs

ACT ONE

EXT. STAR FIELD. NIGHT

As the camera moves through space, past a beautiful, massive planet, a legend appears:

SKARO

The legend then fades and we move past the planet to reveal two moons, which transform into:

LIMBO. BIG CLOSE-UP — THE MASTER'S EYES

The eyes are pure evil, snake-like and glowing.

MASTER
(whispered)

I do hereby make my last will and testament . . .

We move in on one of the eyes as he continues.

If I am to be executed, and thus cruelly deprived of all existence, I ask only that my remains be transported back to my home planet by my rival Time Lord and nemesis – he who calls himself . . . the Doctor.

With this we sweep right into the eye. The iris transforms into:

LIMBO. OVERHEAD SHOT OF PUPIL-LIKE IMAGE

We crane down to reveal what is in fact the skull of a 'spectral-collared' Master, standing in a column of light, awaiting his execution.

DALEK
(off-screen)

You, who dare to challenge the power of the Daleks, have been found guilty as charged. Prepare to die . . .

The Master's eyes suddenly peel back in abject terror.

EXTERMINATE! EXTERMINATE!

In a blast of negative heat, the Master is vaporized, leaving only his screaming eyes, which implode into a spheric crystal that hangs in the limbo for a beat, then suddenly barrels towards us, becoming . . . the main title:

DOCTOR WHO

EXT. INTERDIMENSIONAL VORTEX. MODEL SHOT
As titles come up, we are moving through the heart of an optical illusion. Fantastic geometric shapes open up before us to reveal more shapes within. It is impossible to tell whether we are going backwards or forwards, but we are moving fast, on and on. This is infinity.

Then we see a dark-blue British police lock-up box from the late 1950s barrelling towards us: the TARDIS. As it passes through frame, the grinding sound it makes builds over the score.

INT. THE TARDIS, CONSOLE ROOM
The Doctor's hands carefully transfer the recognizable crystallic remains of the Master's eyes from one container to what looks like a much more secure, small uranium-lined strong box. He screws the lid shut with his sonic screwdriver, then whispers:

DOCTOR

There, that should do it.

We now see the Doctor's weathered and slightly mischievous face. There is an eccentric and lovable gleam in his eyes that we somehow know will never die.

We then close in on the Master's strong box. Intercut with this image are shots of the Doctor settling down for the trip.

Grinding sounds from the time-rotor become more and more intense and suddenly the strong box begins to shake. Then it cracks open and a constantly changing, Morphant-like organic alien being that has formed from the Master's remains emerges

14

and tears off across the TARDIS, unseen by the Doctor. Pausing for a nanosecond, it slithers menacingly into the wires of the inner-core control panel base.

A screen appears:

DESTINATION — GALLIFREY . . .

LOCAL DATELINE — 5725.2

Rassilon era

It suddenly scrambles and a beeping sound is heard.

The Doctor, who has just been settling down to read, moves back to the control panel. We watch his fingers as he throws switches quickly and calmly. The time-rotor suddenly slows down.

We close in on the Doctor's face. He starts to speak to himself, quietly.

Oh, no . . .

From the Doctor's point of view we see the screen again:

CRITICAL TIMING MALFUNCTION —

INSTIGATE AUTOMATIC

EMERGENCY LANDING . . .

Then the screen goes completely blank. The panel sparks and there's a bang. The grinding sound slows even more.

The Doctor races back to where the strong box was and sees that it is wide open. Suddenly he knows what has happened and his eyes fill with fear.

EXT. SAN FRANCISCO SKYLINE. NIGHT

A faint neon glow bounces off a heavy mist that shrouds the night sky. Another legend appears:

SAN FRANCISCO. DECEMBER 30TH 1999

The familiar sparkling skyline of San Francisco rises up into frame.

INT. SAN FRANCISCO APARTMENT. NIGHT.

The head of a fish is being chopped from its body. We are in a small apartment, with an elderly Chinese couple as they prepare their evening meal.

EXT. ROSE ALLEY, CHINATOWN. NIGHT

This deserted back alley is one of many that branch off into the complex web of streets that make up San Francisco's Chinatown.

Off-screen the sound of running feet is suddenly heard, and we see Chang Lee running with two other Chinese kids (they are about seventeen years old) down the alley at the back of a store.

Lee is fifteen but looks older. With him, nothing is wasted, nothing at all. His wiry limbs move fast. Suddenly behind them, car headlights flare into view and they run even faster still.

We see that they are heading towards a barbed-wire-topped mesh gate that divides Rose Alley. They clamber up and over as quickly as they can, just before the car reaches them. Safe on the other side, they start firing weapons at the car.

These kids are as tough and violent as the people who are chasing them. The car immediately slams into reverse and backs away. Fast.

Lee and his gang are moving forward triumphantly when they stop dead. Terror fills their eyes. They have been led into a trap! Waiting there are four other, older Chinese gangsters, armed with automatic machine-guns. The gangsters open fire immediately. With no time to reload their weapons, Lee & Co. dive for cover in all directions.

Lee dives under a pile of wood and trash cans. He looks out and can see that his two friends have been killed.

LEE

No!!

Lee has blown his hiding place. He ducks back in as all the guns turn towards him and open fire, smashing the wood and cans around him to smithereens. He knows his cover won't last long. He screams, terrified, as he desperately tries to reload.

In the same instant, a strange grinding sound fills the already noisy air. Trash swirls up in the foreground and the TARDIS materializes between him and the firepower.

As soon as it becomes solid enough for the bullets to bounce off rather than through it, the door opens. The Doctor bursts out and immediately takes three bullets that were meant for Lee! He gasps in pain, then pulls the door shut behind him as he falls to the ground. The firing stops abruptly.

The attacking gangsters are amazed at what they have seen. A car races up behind them, now entering the alley from the other direction. They pile into it and speed away from the scene.

In the immediate aftermath there is silence. Then a dog is faintly heard barking in the distance. Then traffic can be heard. Lee slowly emerges from behind the TARDIS, eyes peeled, shaking like a leaf. He stares at the strange box that has saved his life. He glances back to his dead friends and his brow furrows in anguish. Then he hears a groan. It is the Doctor.

Lee kneels down beside the stranger. The Doctor is still alive – just.

DOCTOR
(gasps)

. . . timing malfunction . . .

The Doctor looks back to the TARDIS. From his point of view we see the Master Morphant squeezing its way out of the keyhole of the door of the TARDIS.

Stop it! Stop it!

LEE

What?

Lee turns to see what the Doctor is looking at — the door of the TARDIS. There is no Master Morphant. Lee hesitates, then looks back and sees that the Doctor has passed out.

Off-screen the sound of a police siren starts. Lee cuts a strangely heroic silhouette against the busy Chinatown that lies beyond. He speaks quietly.

Hold in there, old guy. Chang Lee will help you . . .

EXT. ROSE ALLEY, CHINATOWN. NIGHT
Unseen on the pavement nearby, the Master Morphant is growing with every second. It side-winds back into the swirling shadows. Its sinister eyes glow with evil. The sound of police and ambulance sirens gets louder.

EXT. AMBULANCE. NIGHT
Rain battles with the windscreen wipers. Sirens scream as the ambulance weaves its way through the blurred lights of the downtown traffic.

INT. AMBULANCE. NIGHT
Lee is sitting in the back next to the Doctor, who is being worked on by a paramedic, Bruce.

LEE

Is he going to live?

BRUCE
(working)

What a mess —
  He looks across to Lee.
You know this guy?

LEE
(lying)

Yeah . . . we were just passing —

                            BRUCE
Is he rich? 'Cause where we're going, he'd better be rich.
Here, sign these for him.

   Bruce throws various forms at Lee, who looks uneasy.

                            LEE
I don't sign anything, Mister —

                            BRUCE
It's just a release. Sign it or he'll die.

   Lee swallows, then slowly looks at a form.

                            LEE
What's the date?

                            BRUCE
December 30th.

                            LEE
                        (filling it in)
1999 . . .

CLOSE-UP — LEE'S HAND
*Filling in the surname, he writes Smith. Then he hesitates over
the forename before writing John.*

EXT. WALKER GENERAL HOSPITAL. NIGHT
*The ambulance drives up and pulls to a halt outside ER
Reception.*

CLOSE-UP — AT THE DRIVER'S FEET
*As the ambulance comes to a halt, something slides forward
along the floor and stops beside the gas pedal. Unnoticed, it is
the Master Morphant.*

INT. HOSPITAL, ER RECEPTION. NIGHT
The Doctor is being rushed out of the ambulance by the driver

and Bruce and taken into the ER reception area. Lee is following a group comprising two nurses, Curtis (twenty-six) and Wheeler (thirty-two), and a resident, Salinger (thirty-seven), as they take over from the ambulance drivers.

BRUCE
(speaking quickly)

Three gunshot wounds – heart's going crazy – he must'a taken something.

SALINGER

Get him into stall eight!

INT. AMBULANCE. NIGHT
The Master Morphant is moving into the back of the ambulance.

INT. HOSPITAL, TRAUMA ROOM. NIGHT
The Doctor, looking almost dead, is put under the massive X-ray machine, which blasts off a quick chest shot in a flash of light.

A second later we see X-rays being clipped to a lightbox.

CURTIS

Two hearts.

WHEELER

One bullet went straight through his shoulder, no damage. The other two are in his left leg –

CURTIS

Look! Two hearts.

WHEELER

What?

SALINGER

As if! It's a double exposure.

Salinger whips the negative off the lightbox, then smiles.

Let's get those bullets out then.

INT. AMBULANCE. NIGHT

The Master Morphant slides into the paramedic's abandoned coat pocket.

INT. HOSPITAL, TRAUMA ROOM. NIGHT

A shining tray: two bullets drop into the tray.

WHEELER

Heart's still going like crazy.

SALINGER

We'd better bring in cardiology.

CURTIS

Who's on tonight?

SALINGER
(smiles)

Grace Kelly . . .

INT. OPERA HOUSE. NIGHT

Close-up on a pair of opera glasses, and the beautiful face behind.

Through the glasses we see scene from Puccini's Madame Butterfly *and hear the famous aria 'One Fine Day'.*

Dr Grace Holloway (between thirty and thirty-five) lowers the opera glasses, touched by the drama of the opera. As Salinger quipped, she does indeed look like a young Grace Kelly, especially in this setting.

Grace's pager suddenly beeps loudly in her bag. As she struggles to turn it off, we see the guy she's with looking on disapprovingly.

INT. HOSPITAL CORRIDOR. NIGHT

Grace enters, sweeping down the corridor wearing a stunning gown.

INT. HOSPITAL, OPERATING PREP. ROOM. NIGHT

Grace enters, still wearing her opera clothes and holding her shoes in her hands.

As she changes into her operating gear, she's brought up to date by the resident.

SALINGER

. . . fibrillation at 300.

GRACE

No blockages showing?

SALINGER

No.

GRACE

X-rays?

SALINGER

NG.

GRACE

What?

SALINGER

Double exposed. Every time we try –

GRACE

Then try again.

SALINGER

We're getting a new machine up. It'll take another half-hour.

GRACE

No time for that. We'd better get moving –

CURTIS
(entering with phone)

Dr Holloway? It's Brian.

The phone is put to her ear as another member of the team gloves and gowns her.

22

GRACE

Yeah . . . I'm sorry . . . I'm on call . . . What should I do, ignore it?

Curtis gives her a look, like she's heard this before. In the background we see that the Doctor is being wheeled in.

Brian . . . I *had* to go . . . Oh, *don't* say that . . . Brian. Wait till I get back . . . Brian!

The line has gone dead.

Curtis looks at her sympathetically.

CURTIS

Gee . . . I'm sorry . . .

INT. HOSPITAL, OPERATING ROOM. NIGHT

GRACE

Micro-surgical probe . . .

We get a close look at the micro-surgical probe as it is passed to Grace to be inserted into the Doctor's cardiovascular system.

And straight to the third act.

Fingers fast-wind the boom box to the third act. Switches on. The Puccini fills the air . . . The Doctor's eyes open.

DOCTOR
(whispered)

Puccini . . . *Madame Butterfly* . . .

The swirling operating lights, people in masks . . .

Whatever you're about to do . . . stop.

Grace comes into frame. Looking down at us, she glances at the Doctor's chart. His name is there.

GRACE

Mr Smith? You're going to be OK.

DOCTOR

No. I'm not human – I'm not the same as you –

23

GRACE
(smiles)

No one's the same as me, Mr Smith –

DOCTOR

Please! I need a beryllium atomic clock.

Grace glances at Salinger. Salinger indicates that the Doctor must be crazy and Grace nods imperceptibly. The bleeping gets louder.

This is 1999, isn't it?

SALINGER

We can't wait any longer, Grace . . .

Grace nods and Salinger places a mask over the Doctor's mouth.

DOCTOR

Wait! I'm not human –

GRACE

Don't try to speak. We've taken those bullets out of you. Now I'm just going to find out what's making your heart so wild – then I'm going to fix it. I've done hundreds of these. OK, Salinger.

Salinger injects the anaesthetic. The Doctor struggles and they have to hold him. The music is turned up. The anaesthetic takes effect and he relaxes. They secure the mask to his face and let go. Then suddenly the Doctor sits bolt upright, speaking through the mask.

DOCTOR

. . . timing malfunction . . . the Master . . .

Grace comes very close and strokes his forehead soothingly.

He's out there . . .

The Doctor's eyes start to roll upwards and his body falls back on to the table. He controls his eyes and looks straight at her, frightened.

I've got to stop him.

She smiles back at him without having understood a word he's said — the music is too loud. The Doctor's eyes roll up as he goes under.

GRACE
(to Salinger)

Somehow, I don't think this guy's name is Mr Smith, do you?

INT. HOSPITAL, OPERATING ROOM OBSERVATION GALLERY. NIGHT

The administrator of the hospital, Dr Roger Swift, is showing some investors around. They look as though they have just arrived from a fund-raiser.

SWIFT

And here we have an electro-physiology being performed by one of our senior cardiologists. Dr Holloway will insert a micro-surgical probe into the patient's artery, then search out the short-circuiting part that is causing the fibrillation, and just so that you know your money is being well spent, she will blast it with lasers.

The investors laugh politely.

INT. HOSPITAL, OPERATING ROOM. NIGHT

Grace is working hard, moving the micro-surgical unit through the Doctor. The ECG is bleeping fast in the corner. Pumps are going up and down.

Grace gives a big sigh.

SALINGER

So, is Brian threatening to leave again?

GRACE

He won't.

SALINGER

This is becoming a habit, Grace. Look, if you want a replacement, I'm house-trained.

GRACE

Forget it, Salinger.

SALINGER
(sarcastic)

Why, thank you . . .

Grace smiles beneath her mask.

GRACE
(quietly)

That's strange.

SALINGER

What?

GRACE

Déjà vu – where am I?

SALINGER

Sub-clavian –

GRACE

But I should be in the brachiocephalic.

SALINGER

Not unless this man is a donkey.

The nurses laugh.

GRACE
(deadly serious)

Then I *am* lost. Let me try something.

She presses a button. The Doctor's body jolts violently.

SALINGER

Massive seizure!

The ECG is all over the place. The Doctor's body jolts again, even more violently this time.

Get the probe out of there –

GRACE

I'm trying!

CURTIS

Picture's out —

GRACE

Dammit!

WHEELER

We're dropping off fast —

SALINGER

Just pull it out!

She tries to get the micro-surgical unit out again.

Come to me! *Come to me!*

SALINGER

Get it out of there!

The Doctor flat-lines. Alarms sound. We see Grace's fright-ened eyes. She looks at her empty hands.

GRACE

It's no good. I can't get it out of him.

SALINGER

Grace . . . he's flat-lining —

GRACE

I got *lost* in there —

SALINGER

He's flat-lining!

GRACE

What?

She's too late. Salinger already has the paddles in his hands.

SALINGER

Clear.

Everyone stands back as Salinger delivers a shock to the Doctor. Grace looks up to the gallery and from her point of view we see Swift hurriedly ushering all the investors out of the viewing rooms. He looks very unhappy.

*Grace is backing away in a state of shock. The Doctor is still
flat-lining.*

Give me 300 —

CURTIS

300.

*He tries again . . . and again . . . and again. We hold on
Grace. What did she do wrong? This is a nightmare. Salinger
turns and looks at her.*

SALINGER

Time of death?

CURTIS

10.03.

GRACE

I got lost — I want to see those X–rays now!

SALINGER
(reaching to hold her)

Grace —

*She pushes him away, then, pulling off her gloves and her
mask, storms out of the operating room.*

INT. HOSPITAL, GRACE'S OFFICE. NIGHT
*The Doctor's things, in a brown-paper bag, are being put down
on the desk by Wheeler.*

WHEELER

This is all his stuff. No identification there either.

GRACE
(quietly off-screen)

Tag him as a John Doe and book him for an autopsy.

WHEELER

You want me to bring that kid in. Maybe he can give us
an identification —

We see Grace staring at the X-ray that is clipped to the light-box.

. . . Doctor?

                    GRACE

Sure.

While Wheeler goes to find Lee, Grace looks more closely at the X-ray. A terrified look of realization comes over her face. She speaks in a whisper.

This is no double exposure . . .

INT. HOSPITAL CORRIDOR. NIGHT

Lee, who has been waiting all this time, is found by Wheeler and led towards Grace's office.

INT. HOSPITAL, GRACE'S OFFICE. NIGHT

Lee is led into the room. Grace is looking through the Doctor's possessions. She picks out a bag of sweets and puts them to one side.

                    GRACE

You a friend of Mr Smith?

                    LEE

Yeah . . . Is he OK?

                    GRACE

Look . . . There were complications and I'm afraid he didn't make it. Sorry.

Lee's jaw clenches, then he speaks quietly.

                    LEE

It's OK.

Lee eyes the bag full of possessions on the table. Grace watches him suspiciously . . .

I'll tell his family. These his things?

GRACE

Yeah.

LEE

I'll take them.

Grace senses a false note as he looks inside the bag, assessing what's there . . .

GRACE

Maybe we should contact the family ourselves –

LEE

No, Miss, this'll hit them hard. I'll tell them –

GRACE

(confronting him)

You don't know this man at all, do you?

LEE

Yes, I do!

GRACE

Then tell me his real name.

LEE

I gotta go, man –

He starts to head out of the door.

GRACE

Wait.

Lee runs out with the bag of the Doctor's things.

INT. HOSPITAL CORRIDOR. NIGHT

Lee races through the busy corridor. Grace chases after him.

GRACE

Hey! Someone stop him.

One or two of the other nurses start to chase after him, but Lee is too fast for them and he manages to make it out of the front entrance before anyone can catch him.

EXT. SAN FRANCISCO. NIGHT
A view of the city.

INT. BRUCE'S APARTMENT, BEDROOM. NIGHT
The air is filled with the loud snores of Bruce, the paramedic, who even after twenty years of marriage is still keeping his wife, Miranda (forty-three), awake. She is tossing and turning, going through the usual insomniac routine as she tries to get some sleep. Finally she turns away in disgust, staring at the neon outside.

INT. BRUCE'S APARTMENT, BEDROOM FLOOR. NIGHT
The ever-growing Master Morphant winds its way out of the folds of Bruce's abandoned paramedic jacket, slides up the bedpost and on to the bed. Then it slithers silently towards Bruce, unseen by Miranda.

CLOSE-UP — BRUCE
His snoring gets louder. Suddenly, the Morphant slides into his open mouth, gagging him into immediate silence.

CLOSE-UP — MIRANDA
She looks surprised for an instant, then, as the silence holds, a smile crosses her face.

CLOSE-UP — BRUCE
His eyes contort, bulging, popping. He is being killed from the inside by the evil Morphant. His eyes close. There is absolute silence.

CLOSE-UP — MIRANDA
She closes her eyes . . . sleep at last.

INT. HOSPITAL MORGUE. NIGHT

We follow the Doctor's body as it is wheeled into the morgue by Pete. Another porter, Ted, helps him as they prepare the body for cold-storage.

PETE

You going anywhere special for New Year's Eve?

TED

Fancy-dress party.

PETE

Yeah, me too. Who are you going as?

TED

Wild Bill Hickok.

Pete starts filling out the papers and attaching a tag to the dead toe. It reads JOHN DOE.

PETE

(talking to the body)

John Doe on the toe. We got a nice autopsy booked for you first thing in the morning, Mister, followed by a sauna *or* a Swedish herbal wrap. What would be your pleasure?

Pete looks up at the clock as he fills in the date.

One a.m. Hey, it's December 31st 1999! Party on.

We see the Doctor's icy-blue face as it is covered up by the shroud. Then we follow the whole body as it is slid into the freezer and slammed into the darkness.

INT. HOSPITAL MORGUE, FREEZER. NIGHT

Behind the shroud we can see a strange light start to glow. It looks like a mini-tidal wave swirling out from within, a sweep of mini-stars and galaxies, curling and weaving through the dead organism. Then suddenly the Doctor's hand rips away the shroud.

The whole naked body silently arches back, glowing ethereally.

We curl over the top of it and move in on the face. It literally contorts, morphing, growing, transforming before our eyes. The process looks agonizing and euphoric all at the same time. The new Doctor's face is still timeless, but there is a new strength there and even more wisdom than before. Not a trace of the last Doctor remains. He has a new body.

The new Doctor's eyes blink open, bright and alive, shining in the light of his own rebirth.

INT. HOSPITAL MORGUE. NIGHT

Later on, Pete is back, watching an old black-and-white movie on the TV, when a loud thumping noise comes from the body room. The thumping doesn't stop.

PETE

Ted? That you?

No response. Pete gets up and heads to the body room. The room is dark. For the first time in the scene, we realize that he has been watching a horror movie on the TV. The music is dead right for what we are seeing. He stops at the threshold. The thumping comes again, louder.

Who's there?

Pete realizes that the thumping is coming from the door he slammed shut earlier. He turns on the fluorescent lights before slowly moving inside the room.

The lights gradually flicker to life down the room. He is just about to reach for the door handle when the door smashes open by itself.

The foot sporting the JOHN DOE tag pushes its way out into the pulsating green fluorescent light.

Oh, God! God, no!

Suddenly the Doctor slides his gurney out across the room, sending himself crashing into the wall opposite, where his body *collapses into a heap on the floor.*

Pete looks terrified and then his eyes peel back in pure terror as he sees the Doctor rise up, lift himself to his feet and look straight at him. There is a confused expression on his face, risen from the dead. Pete's eyes roll up and he passes out . . .

INT. HOSPITAL CORRIDOR. NIGHT

The Doctor, wearing only his shroud and his JOHN DOE tag, staggers down the darkened corridor. Outside rain streams down the windows, sending a rippling light over the whole scene. He moves past a sign that says NO ENTRY.

INT. HOSPITAL WARD. NIGHT

Abandoned beds are piled up in the centre of a darkened ward that is under reconstruction. Outside the storm is at its height. Thunder rolls heavily. Lightning flashes. The Doctor staggers into the ward and, breathless, stops at the end. A sharp darting pain in his side from the operation troubles him. He winces. Then, a sharp intake of breath as the lightning flashes and he sees his own reflection in a broken mirror. He moves close to the mirror. He looks more carefully at his face, while outside it rains harder and harder. The rippling light from outside moves faster. The Doctor tentatively feels his features with his bony hands. He whispers.

DOCTOR

Who am I?

Then the lightning strikes again in silence, a long flash, in which we cut to a wide shot. The Doctor's shadow is thrown, gigantic, across the hospital wall. In silhouette we see his tortured head swaying back into the rippling shadows of the pouring rain. Then his very soul thunders:

WHO AM I?

INT. BRUCE'S APARTMENT. NIGHT

In the same lightning flash the dead Bruce's eyes open in the dark to reveal that he has been totally possessed by the Master! These are the same evil eyes that we saw at the start of the movie . . .

FADE OUT

ACT TWO

EXT. GOLDEN GATE BRIDGE, DAWN
Unbelievably beautiful dawn shots of the city and the bridge.

INT. GRACE'S OFFICE. DAWN
Grace's sleeping face in the soft dawn light. She has been working hard all night and didn't go home. Nearby, the Doctor's X-ray is still on the lightbox.

INT. HOSPITAL, MORGUE CHANGING ROOM. DAWN
The Doctor's feet enter frame, the JOHN DOE tag still attached to his toe. Checking that the place is empty, he moves inside. Distinctive evidence of Pete marks his locker.

The Doctor goes through the clothes in the locker room. The only ones that take his fancy are the Wild Bill Hickok clothes that Ted was going to wear to the party. Breathing fast, eyes still alight with fear and pain, he quickly tries them on, looking in a mirror.

EXT. ROSE ALLEY, CHINATOWN. DAWN
Lee is going through the Doctor's things. A yo-yo, a pocket watch, a sonic screwdriver and finally a shining, strangely shaped key. Lee turns the key between his shivering fingers. Then he slowly makes his way back down the alley towards the TARDIS. He stops and watches the people go by. He is waiting until the coast is clear . . .

Police tape marks off the area of the gangland killing from the previous night. The ground is marked where the bodies fell. In the middle of it all, strewn with debris from the fight, stands the

TARDIS. *A lone squad car passes nearby, slows down and then moves on.*

INT. BRUCE'S APARTMENT. DAWN
Miranda's eyes open. Everything is peaceful. She smiles as she sees what she thinks is Bruce, her husband, standing naked looking at himself in the dresser mirror, his back to her. She can't see his reflection and neither can we.

BRUCE/MASTER
(whispered)

This body won't last long . . .
He takes a deep breath.
I need the Doctor's body.

MIRANDA
(smiles, then speaks softly)

No snoring. A sense of humour. You don't need a doctor, honey. Come back to bed.
The Master/Bruce is about to turn and look at her, but he hesitates. Then speaks quietly.

BRUCE/MASTER

My name isn't 'honey' . . .
We just see the back of his head during the following exchange.

MIRANDA

What should I call you then?

BRUCE/MASTER

'Master' will do.

CLOSE-UP — MIRANDA
Silently, she comes up behind him and hugs him.

MIRANDA

'Master' . . . come back to bed.
He turns to her. When she sees his face, she screams!

40

CLOSE-UP — THE MASTER'S NEW FACE

Miranda's scream intensifies. The Master raises one finger to his lips and with the other hand he reaches off-screen to Miranda. The screaming is cut short . . . Silence. The Master slowly closes his eyes.

INT. HOSPITAL MORGUE. DAY
Grace and Pete are both in the morgue.

> PETE

It wasn't the same guy!

> GRACE

Sounds to me like you saw the man who stole the body.

> PETE

But he was wearing a shroud and a JD tag on his toe!

> GRACE

Somehow I don't believe the second coming happens here . . .

> PETE

Right . . . You think he'd go to a better hospital? I know what. I'm going home.

He gets up to go.

> GRACE

Stop by psychiatric on the way and pick up some more mind-altering drugs, Pete.

> PETE

Yeah, sure.

Grace is left staring at the hinges that were ripped from the freezer door by the regenerating Doctor.

INT. HOSPITAL CORRIDOR. DAY
Grace emerges a little later from an elevator and sweeps past the Doctor, who is sitting in a long line of patients totally unnoticed.

We see his full costume for the first time. He has a lost look on his face, no shoes and the tag on the toe of his bare feet.

His eye is caught by Grace's face as she passes.

FLASH CUT — FROM THE OPERATION
Grace's face looking down at us, Puccini in the background.

INT. HOSPITAL CORRIDOR. DAY
There is now a look of recognition on the Doctor's face. He gets up and slowly starts walking towards Grace.

GRACE

Can you get SFPD in on this? Some creep's made off with the John Doe that died last night.

CURTIS

Eeeew — body-snatchers!

The Doctor is about to interrupt her when Swift, the administrator, comes between them. The Doctor backs away.

SWIFT

Don't call the police yet, Curtis. Dr Holloway, can you give me some time?

The Doctor's eyes burn as if he's starting to realize something.

DOCTOR

Time . . . Time!

A clock on the wall flips the time: 10.22.

INT. HOSPITAL, GRACE'S OFFICE. DAY
Swift is taking down the Doctor's X-ray from the lightbox that we saw earlier.

SWIFT

We don't need to advertise our mistakes, do we?

GRACE

What are you saying?

SWIFT
(looking)

Two hearts. No wonder you got lost —

GRACE

Exactly —

SWIFT

Or maybe this really is a double exposure, Grace. Either way, I can't afford to lose you.

He gets out a pair of scissors and cuts the X-ray in two.

GRACE

What are you doing?

SWIFT

What you should have done last night.

GRACE

Am I having a bad dream here? I lose a patient, then I lose his body, and now you destroy the only proof —

SWIFT

— that you were careless.

GRACE

That I had no way of knowing —

SWIFT

Stop! A man died last night because you lost your way.

GRACE

You bet I did. You've seen that X-ray, the guy had two hearts!

SWIFT

But now, without a body, without any records, no one need know he was here.

GRACE

You can't do that!

SWIFT
(smiles)

Let me take care of this, Grace.

GRACE

No!

SWIFT

Believe me, this is the best way for all of us.

GRACE

But what *was* he? How can we *learn* from him? I have to find his body.

SWIFT

And I have to keep this hospital open.

GRACE

No. *No!* If you do this, I'll quit.

SWIFT

You don't mean that.

A beat. Grace looks at him.

INT. HOSPITAL. DAY

Grace heads towards the elevator, struggling with all the things from her office. It arrives and she gets in. Someone gets in beside her. As the doors close, we see it is the Doctor.

INT. HOSPITAL. ELEVATOR. DAY

Grace keeps her eyes fixed on the indicator. The Doctor is watching her. He suddenly points at her.

DOCTOR

Puccini!

Grace smiles, humouring him, then looks away.

We've met before.

GRACE
(shakes her head)

I don't think so.

DOCTOR

I think so . . .
He looks at her, then he speaks quietly.
I know you. You're tired of life, but afraid of dying . . .
Grace avoids eye contract. She sighs.

INT. HOSPITAL. UNDERGROUND PARKING LOT. DAY
The Doctor is following Grace to her car.

DOCTOR

There was music . . . *Madame Butterfly* . . . And you were
there! I saw you last night.

GRACE

Not me.

DOCTOR

I don't know who I am. But I know you know me.

GRACE

Please go away.

DOCTOR

You're my only hope.

GRACE

I'll call security.

DOCTOR

Do you know who I am?

GRACE

I have no idea! Now leave me alone.

DOCTOR

Please help me, you're a doctor —

GRACE

My oath just expired. Now stand back!

The Doctor stops. Grace, using her automatic key ring, unlocks her car, throws her things in the back, gets in as fast as she can and starts the motor.

INT. GRACE'S CAR. DAY
Grace looks around the lot outside. The Doctor has gone. She activates the central locking.

Suddenly the Doctor yells out from the back seat, where he has sneaked in unseen. Grace screams, terrified. The Doctor is doubled over in agony.

GRACE

Out! *Get out!!!*

DOCTOR

My *hearts*!!

He rips back his shirt and thrusts his hand into the space just under his ribs. Grace looks horrified. She starts sounding the car horn.

There's something here!

Something small and slimy, like a tiny snail, is sticking out of his chest. Grace pulls back.

GRACE

Oh, *God*!

DOCTOR
(in agony)

What is it? What *is* it!

The Doctor, terrified, pulls out what's there. It glints — it's a wire, recognizably, the micro-surgical probe we saw the previous night.

Grace takes her fist off the horn. With a ghastly look of recognition on her face, she whispers:

GRACE

It can't be . . .

Two hearts! I have two hearts! Now get me out of here before they kill me again.

We push in on Grace's terrified face . . .

Drive!

Grace looks back into the parking lot.

You've got to help me!

A security man is running towards the car. She slams the gearstick into drive, floors the gas and burns rubber. The Doctor is thrown back. As she speeds out of the parking lot, the Puccini score soars to a crescendo.

INT. HOSPITAL RECEPTION. DAY

Nurse Curtis looks up. She smiles.

CURTIS

Hi, Bruce . . . Why the shades?

The Master, in his new body, is looking down on us, sporting a pair of dark glasses, his long paramedic's jacket, jeans, boots and a distant smile. He speaks quietly.

MASTER

I had a bad night.

Curtis tries to continue working but the Master stares at her.

CURTIS

(unnerved)

Did you want something?

MASTER

Er . . . what happened to the gunshot wound I brought in? I've got orders to move him.

CURTIS.

He died.

MASTER

Oh, yeah. They wanted me to move his body.

Curtis hesitates . . . Is Bruce for real? Then she sees him absent-mindedly pull a fingernail clean off of his little finger. She swallows in disgust.

CURTIS

Bruce, you OK?

MASTER

Where is it?

CURTIS

Haven't you heard? The body's gone. Stolen.
The Master realizes that the Doctor has regenerated, but he can't say this in front of Curtis.

MASTER

OK, so where are his things?

CURTIS

The kid that brought him ran off with them.

MASTER

The Asian child?

CURTIS

'The Asian child' – Bruce, you *are* sick.

MASTER
(smiles a thin smile)

Thank you.
The Master immediately turns and walks out of reception. Curtis looks hurt. What's got into him?

EXT. GOLDEN GATE BRIDGE. DAY
We sweep back from a view of the city from the bridge to reveal the Marin headlands beyond.

DOCTOR

Look at that! San Francisco when it was still inhabited! Amazing . . .

INT. GRACE'S CONDO. DAY

Grace is struggling up the stairs to the living room with the stuff from her office. The Doctor follows.

GRACE

You all right?

DOCTOR
(off-screen)

Much better.

GRACE

Good.

DOCTOR

Now I don't have a piece of primitive wiring inside my cardiovascular system.

Grace sees that half the furniture has gone, alone with loads of other things.

GRACE

I don't believe it! He's taken all his stuff . . .

DOCTOR

Who?

GRACE

Brian.

DOCTOR

Your boyfriend?

Then Grace puts down her things angrily.

GRACE

Ex-boyfriend.

She opens one of her bags and pulls out a stethoscope.

Sit down and open your shirt, I want to listen to your heart.

DOCTOR

Hearts . . .

The Doctor looks around for somewhere to sit. There is nowhere.

GRACE

He took the sofa! Come up here . . .

She leads him up into her area. They sit down next to each other.

DOCTOR

I'm remembering more now.

He sees out of the window as he takes off his shirt.

What a lovely view.

GRACE

Maybe you had selective amnesia, brought on by shock.

DOCTOR

Maybe.

She starts to listen to his chest.

I can't remember.

GRACE

Shh!

Then, as she listens, the Doctor is looking around the apartment. He sees a Da Vinci print on the wall.

DOCTOR

A Da Vinci! He had a terrible cold when he drew that.

GRACE

You're still fibrillating badly.

DOCTOR

No, I'm not. Here . . .

He moves her stethoscope over to the other side of his chest. As Grace listens, the Doctor picks up a CD case from nearby.

I remember – I was *with* Puccini before he died.

GRACE

Name-dropper.

DOCTOR

No. I *was.*

GRACE

Shh. Oh, God . . .

She can hear the other heart.

DOCTOR

See . . . It's not an echo.

Then, looking back to the CD.

I remember, he died before he could finish *Turandot*. It was so sad. Alfano finished it, based on his notes.

Grace looks him in the eyes.

GRACE

Two hearts . . . you were right. Who are you?

DOCTOR

I was dead for too long this time. The anaesthetic almost destroyed the regenerative process.

Grace is getting out a syringe and opening it.

GRACE

(shakily)

Oh, yeah . . . right . . . Look, I'm going to take some of your blood and find out what's going on here.

DOCTOR

No, Grace, don't you see? I have twelve lives –

GRACE

Please! So you're trying to tell me˙that you came back from the dead? Sorry, the dead stay dead. You can't turn back time.

DOCTOR

Yes, you can –

GRACE

I'm not a child – don't talk to me like a child! Only children believe that crap. I'm a doctor!

DOCTOR

But it was a childish dream that made you a doctor. You

dreamt you could hold back death! Isn't that true?

There's a pause. She just looks at him.

DOCTOR

Don't be sad. You will do great things . . .

EXT/INT. THE TARDIS. ROSE ALLEY, CHINATOWN. DAY

The coast is clear. No one is standing near the TARDIS. Clutching the Doctor's things, Lee carefully approaches and puts the key into the keyhole of the door. It fits perfectly. He turns it and opens the door.

LEE

Hello?

His voice echoes. He looks outside and around the box before moving on in . . .

INT. THE TARDIS

Coming off a close-up reaction shot on Lee, we see a vast space with the master control console in the centre. Lee moves right inside, almost to the console, awestruck by the size of the place.

The only light seems to come from outside. Suddenly, the door slams shut behind us and we are plunged into near-darkness. Lee peers back into the echoing shadows, sensing movement but unable to see.

LEE

Who's there?

Then, as if in response, the Master's evil eyes glow back at him through the dark and the Master sweeps towards him.

MASTER

You don't want to know.

As the Master gets closer, so he moves into the ambient dim light from above and Lee recognizes the paramedic he got to know the previous night. He is relieved.

52

Oh, it's you, man – Bruce. Hey, don't scare me like that!
This place is freaky, yeah?

*The Master steps up on to the control console platform. It is
dark save for the timing malfunction warning that continues to
flash. He comes closer.*

MASTER

Lee . . . Chang Lee, isn't that your name?

*Lee steps up on to the platform, but as soon as his feet touch
its surface, the TARDIS glows into life. The Master looks surprised. This is a revelation, a useful one.*

Well, I never . . . The TARDIS *likes* you.

LEE

What do you mean, Bruce?

MASTER

I'm not Bruce, I am merely . . . *inside* his body.

LEE

(not believing)

Oh, yeah . . . So who are you really?

*The Master comes very close to him so he can see his unnat-
ural eyes. They start to glow.. The eyes burn brighter still . . .
white hot!*

*Lee looks seriously, at the Master and then around. This is
really happening.*

*The Master, knowing he's putting one over on Lee, gently
takes the Doctor's things off Lee and looks at them, then at Lee.*

MASTER

Where is he?

LEE

Who?

MASTER

The man you took these things from.

LEE

He's dead. They're mine now —

MASTER

He's not dead! He's stolen my body.

LEE

But —

MASTER

I will die unless we bring him back here, and you're
going to help me do that.

*Lee looks around, scared, realizing that there is no waking up,
no way out . . .*

LEE
(after a beat)

What's in it for me?

MASTER
(almost to himself)

You get to live.

FADE OUT

ACT THREE

EXT. GRACE'S CONDO. NIGHT

INT. GRACE'S CONDO. NIGHT
We go close in on Grace's view through a microscope: the Doctor's blood. She is very busy.

CLOSE–UP — GRACE
She comes up from the eyepiece with an amazed look on her face. Running her hand through her hair, she makes some more notes, then looks across the room at the Doctor. She has been making a lot of experiments.

The Doctor comes downstairs. He has found a pair of loafers and tries them on. He realizes that she is looking at him and smiles.

DOCTOR
They fit. Did these belong to . . .

GRACE
(looking)
Brian? Yeah. Keep them.

DOCTOR
Thanks.
There's a pause as he admires his new shoes.
What do you think of my blood?

GRACE
It's not blood.
The Doctor is twiddling his toes.

DOCTOR
Mmm. Maybe if I walk in them a bit, they'll stretch and

57

I'll get used to them . . .

GRACE

(standing up)

Good idea. Let's go for a walk.

EXT. NEARBY PARK. NIGHT

Grace and the Doctor emerge from her house and head across into a nearby park. The Doctor now has a scarf and maybe even a hat to match, all acquired from Brian's cast-offs. As they walk into the park, away from us, Grace tries to work things out.

GRACE

Maybe you're the result of some weird genetic experiment?

DOCTOR

I don't think so —

GRACE

But you have no recollection of family.

DOCTOR

No. No, wait . . . I do. I remember lying back in the grass with my father on a warm Gallifreyan night —

GRACE

Gallifreyan?

DOCTOR

Gallifrey, yes — That must be where I lived. Now where is that?

GRACE

Never heard of the place. But what do you remember?

DOCTOR

Not much. There was a meteor storm and the sky above us was dancing with lights — purple, green, brilliant yellow . . .

The Doctor's eyes light up as if he's seeing it now. He starts

58

walking a little faster. He smiles to himself.
Yes . . .

What?

These shoes fit perfectly.

INT. THE TARDIS, LIBRARY AREA
The Master is talking to Lee as he searches busily in the library.
He is really selling him a line now. Lee watches in amazement.

MASTER
(searching)
This was all mine until he stole it from me. He should
never have been here.

LEE
You know, I *was* told he was dead.

MASTER
(searching)
Yes, that body has died, but now he's regenerated into
another. My body can do this twelve times and he's taken
most of the regenerations!

LEE
What did he did with them?

MASTER
Unspeakable crimes.

LEE
Like what?

MASTER
Genghis Khan.

LEE
What about him?

59

MASTER

That was him.

LEE

No way!

MASTER

I'm no saint, but he's evil. And he's doing it all with my body! I was on the verge of stopping him when we arrived — There they are!

The Master pulls open a cupboard full of little bags.

What do you want, Lee?

LEE

What do you mean?

MASTER

If you could have anything, anything at all, what would that be?

LEE

I don't know. A million dollars?

MASTER

Only a million?

LEE

OK . . . Two?

MASTER

Think bigger!

LEE

A billion!

MASTER

And what would that buy you?

LEE

Power . . .

The Master smiles to himself, as if to say: Humans!

But how can you give that to me?

The Master throws one of the bags from the cupboard over to Lee. Lee opens it, awed.

Gold dust . . .

MASTER

You get the rest when I get my body back. Deal?

LEE

Deal.

The Master heads off. Lee hesitates, then pockets another bag and follows him.

INT. THE TARDIS, CLOISTER ROOM

Lee pushes a massive door with his fingers and it flies open with almost supernatural speed. Old leaves and debris swirl up in front of him.

LEE

Wow! How did I do that?

The Master smiles.

MASTER

I told you . . . the TARDIS likes you.

They move into a very beautiful space with a cathedral feel to it. The Master leads Lee up a long ramp.

The Cloister Room.

LEE

Awesome . . .

MASTER

Here . . .

We move back to reveal they are approaching a highly ornate, crypt-like structure shaped like a closed eye. At each corner four six-foot-tall, antique dental mirrors stick out of four mounds that also look like little eyes.

This is the Eye of Harmony . . . the heart of this place. Everything gets its power from here.

The mirrors are reflecting beams of light in criss-cross patterns across the Cloister Room. It's very beautiful.

LEE

How can it help us find him?

MASTER

This eye used to belong to me, now it belongs to him. If we can open it, we'll find him.

LEE

Cool. So you going to open it?

MASTER

No, you are. See if you can pull a reflector staff from its mooring.

LEE

One of these?

He pulls at one of the staffs and it comes out of the stone mooring. Light shoots up from the remaining hole in a straight beam. The Master smiles. It is as if Arthur had just casually pulled the sword from the stone.

MASTER

Now look into the beam of light. If the TARDIS really likes you, the Eye will open.

LEE

(hesitates)

Why don't you look?

MASTER

You drew the staff from the stone.

Lee slowly moves close to the surface of the stone. He nervously puts his eyes into the beam of light. The big eye starts to open, as if the stone were becoming organic tissue . . .

Lee stares into the light, smiling, proud.

EXT. PARK NEAR GRACE'S CONDO. NIGHT
It is misty. Suddenly the Doctor stops. He puts his hand to his head and his eyes roll back.

GRACE

What is it?

DOCTOR

Something's happening.
  She looks into his face, holding his arms.

GRACE

Hey?

INT. THE TARDIS, CLOISTER ROOM
The light is swirling and strange singing comes out of the Eye. Lee peers in.

MASTER

What do you see?
  We look into the eye from Lee's point of view and can see seven different faces forming a ring.

LEE

There's the guy I took to the hospital.

MASTER

The Doctor's past lives.

LEE

The Doctor?

MASTER

That's what he calls himself.

EXT. PARK NEAR GRACE'S CONDO. NIGHT
The Doctor suddenly looks euphoric.

DOCTOR
(quietly)

I . . . I know who I am . . .

He suddenly kisses Grace – long and passionately. It's incredibly romantic, with the swirling mist and the growing winter darkness all around them.

INT. THE TARDIS, CLOISTER ROOM
It is as if, with the kiss itself, a new face is forming in the centre of the Eye of Harmony: the new Doctor. Music swells.

EXT. PARK NEAR GRACE'S CONDO. NIGHT
The Doctor's and Grace's lips part. She looks at him, shocked.
                    DOCTOR
I am the Doctor!
                    GRACE
                (breathless)
Good . . . Now do that again . . .
   Then Grace suddenly smiles and pulls the Doctor back into another embrace. She kisses him passionately.

INT. THE TARDIS, CLOISTER ROOM
The Master is studying the new Doctor's face for the first time, his eyes alight. Suddenly there's a deep rumbling. We see the new Doctor's face moving towards us, growing bigger and bigger.
   The image of the Doctor's eye suddenly wraps around us, projected so that it fills the entire Cloister Room.

CLOSE–UP – LEE AND THE MASTER
Their faces are alive with the projected pattern of the Doctor's retina. Lee smiles at its beauty. The Master is looking at the holographic patterns that surround them, his eyes gleaming. It is as if he's found the Holy Grail.
                    MASTER
See *that*? The retinal structure of the eye . . . The Doctor

is half human!
He laughs.
No wonder . . .
Then there's another blast of light.

EXT. PARK NEAR GRACE'S CONDO. NIGHT
The Doctor pulls back from the embrace. Grace is surprised, but she's still with him.

> DOCTOR

No!

> GRACE

What?

> DOCTOR

I saw him . . . The Master is here.

> GRACE

The Master? What are you talking about?
Grace goes to hold him again, but he pushes her away. Now she is quite shocked.

> DOCTOR

He's planning to take my body, so that he will live and I will die. Oh, no!
His eyes widen.
No!
We see Grace looking straight at us, shocked. Her face flashes to white-out, losing all its features.

CLOSE-UP — THE DOCTOR

> DOCTOR

He's opened the Eye of Harmony!

INT. THE TARDIS, CLOISTER ROOM
Grace's face materializes, looming up at us out of the Eye of

Harmony.

GRACE

(desperately trying to reach him)

What is the Eye of Harmony, tell me?

DOCTOR

(off-screen)

Wait —

MASTER

There! We're seeing what he's seeing.

LEE

I know that woman —
Suddenly Grace's head disappears.

EXT. PARK NEAR GRACE'S CONDO. NIGHT
The Doctor has his eyes closed tight. He is speaking fast.

DOCTOR

I'm shutting my eyes so he can't see you, Grace! But it
may be too late.

GRACE

What is the Eye of Harmony?

DOCTOR

It's the power source at the heart of the TARDIS.

GRACE

The TARDIS? What is the TARDIS?

DOCTOR

The TARDIS is my spaceship. It carries me through
space and time.
*This hits Grace like a bullet. Her heart sinks as she looks at
the man who has just kissed her. She was growing close to him
and now he's talking about spaceships!*
T – A – R – D – I – S. It stands for Time and Relative
Dimension in Space.

Grace starts to back away, unsure.

GRACE

And this Master . . . is he like the Devil?

DOCTOR

No! The Master is a rival Time Lord.

GRACE

A Time Lord . . . Oh, my God!

DOCTOR

Pure evil. I was bringing home his remains from Skaro, where his final incarnation had been exterminated by the Daleks. Or so we thought!

Grace's jaw drops – total disbelief, which, of course, the Doctor can't see.

GRACE

Oh, God . . . You really *are* insane, aren't you?

DOCTOR

But he wasn't dead! It's . . . It's a trap, don't you see! He wants me to look into the Eye . . .

INT. THE TARDIS, CLOISTER ROOM

The Master and Lee listen to the Doctor's voice, which fills the space.

DOCTOR

If I look into the Eye of Harmony, my soul will be destroyed and he will take my body!

MASTER

Listen to all those lies!

LEE

How could she believe him?

MASTER

Pure evil, that's how.

67

EXT. PARK NEAR GRACE'S CONDO. NIGHT

Grace is backing away from the Doctor, who still has his eyes shut.

GRACE

I don't want to deal with this.

DOCTOR

Please, Grace, listen carefully –

GRACE

No, that's *enough*!

DOCTOR

If the Eye of Harmony remains open for too long, this planet will be sucked through it.

Grace backs away, frightened, while the Doctor speaks fast.

Grace! I must fix the timing mechanism on the TARDIS so I can close the Eye. I need an atomic clock. Can you help me find one, Grace?

She starts to run away. The Doctor shouts after her:

Grace!

INT. THE TARDIS, CLOISTER ROOM

MASTER

So that's how he intends to destroy me.

LEE

How?

MASTER

We must get to the Doctor before he finds a clock . . .

LEE

I *know* that woman. She was the surgeon that operated on him last night!

MASTER

If we find her, then we'll find him.

They leave the Cloister Room. The only light that remains

comes from the eye — a soft, swirling effect.

EXT. PARK NEAR GRACE'S CONDO. NIGHT
The Doctor slowly opens his eyes.
From his point of view we see the park and the bay at night. In the distance he sees Grace's house. She is heading back inside, shutting the door behind her.
The Doctor races after her as fast as he can.

EXT. GRACE'S CONDO. NIGHT
Grace is looking nervously out of the downstairs window. We can see the Doctor's approach reflected in the glass.

INT. GRACE'S HALLWAY. NIGHT
Grace double-bolts the front door and attaches chains to everything. Then there's a massive thump! She jumps back, terrified.
GRACE

You stay away from me!

EXT. GRACE'S FRONT DOOR. NIGHT
The Doctor tries to reason with her.
DOCTOR

Grace, please just let me in.
GRACE

No!
DOCTOR

Grace . . . If you let me in, we can calm down, have a cup of tea and talk about this reasonably.
GRACE

Sure, Time Lord to Earthling.
DOCTOR

That's right! I am a Time Lord . . .

GRACE

I thought you were a doctor?

DOCTOR

I though *you* were a doctor!

Grace hesitates, thinking for a moment.

GRACE

Listen, I'm going to call for an ambulance to take you back to the psychiatric ward, from which you obviously escaped.

DOCTOR

Grace, we don't have the time for this. The Eye of Harmony is open, and if I don't close it and get my TARDIS and the Master off this planet, this planet will no longer exist. I reckon we've got until midnight.

Grace closes her eyes in despair

GRACE

I'm going to call for an ambulance.

She walks into the downstairs living room. The Doctor is left standing on the other side of the locked door. He sniffs the air, slowly. He steps across to the window, looking into the living room, and watches as Grace calls on the phone. He can't hear what she is saying.

INT. GRACE'S LIVING ROOM. NIGHT

GRACE

Yes, I'll hold . . .

She looks at the table, where the remains of the micro-surgical probe she took from the Doctor earlier are lying. She sees the notes about the blood and the cardiograph print-outs that are strewn everywhere. Suddenly there's a knock on the glass behind her. She turns around and jumps when she sees the Doctor.

70

Grace, I'm going to prove to you that the Eye of Harmony is open. Look at this . . .

He knocks on the hard glass, then he pushes against it with the flat of his palm.

You see . . . already the molecular structure of the planet is changing. At first in subtle ways —

Grace blinks as she sees him literally push the glass, which starts to stretch.

— then soon in catastrophic ways.

He pushes his arm and then bit by bit his whole body into and through the glass, as if he were pushing his way through cling-film. Until there he is, standing in the room.

By midnight tonight, this planet will be pulled inside-out. There will be *nothing* left!

Grace stares at the Doctor, stunned. She talks shakily into the phone.

GRACE

Hi . . . Yes . . . I need an ambulance as soon as possible. This is Dr Grace Holloway. I'm going to need a bed in psychiatric . . . Better make that two.

INT. AMBULANCE/EXT. HOSPITAL. NIGHT

We are inside the back of an empty ambulance. The doors open and a gurney is pushed inside by an ambulance driver. The doors are slammed shut again.

The camera pans, following his steps as he comes around to the driver's door, opens it and climbs into the driver's seat. He gets out his keys and puts them in the ignition. He is about to turn the key when without warning he is attacked from behind by some unearthly force.

71

INT. GRACE'S LIVING ROOM. NIGHT

The Doctor is weighing himself on a set of scales that Grace had out earlier for the experiments. Grace is watching at the window. The TV is on in the background.

                    DOCTOR

I've lost twenty pounds

                    GRACE
                (humouring him)

Congratulations.

                    DOCTOR
                    (gravely)

In twenty minutes. It's starting.

                    GRACE
                    (joking)

You'd make a fortune in the weight-loss business, Doctor . . .

The Doctor picks up the remote and starts flipping channels feverishly. Grace is watching out for the ambulance, muttering to herself.

Come on!

The Doctor stops at a news programme. He notices his Jelly Babies, the sweets that Grace took out of his bag in the hospital. He chews one, as he watches, then pockets the bag.

                    ANCHOR WOMAN
                    (on TV)

'And now for that item we promised you about "The Millennium Effect", as some are calling it. Since early this evening, Bay Area tides have risen to levels that break all records for this time of year. Flood warnings have gone out along the Napa and Russian rivers and get this, in Hawaii it has started snowing!'

DOCTOR

Look at that, Grace. See!

TV ANCHOR

'Now, you maybe wondering what this has to do with the millennium. We've been told that the freak conditions are due to very slight fluctuations in the Earth's gravitational pull – fluctuations that apparently only happen once every thousand years . . .'

The Doctor laughs at this as the TV anchor hands over to a field reporter. Night shots of a reporter standing in front of blizzard flash on the screen.

DOCTOR

I love humans . . . the way they see patterns in things that aren't there.

Grace looks at him, liking this thought, then she sees the ambulance pulling up outside. She gets a coat.

TV ANCHOR

'And when we come back, we'll be showing you where the wealthiest and most fashionable San Franciscans are going tonight to see in the new millennium.'

TV CO-ANCHOR

'Didn't you say they're going to see a clock being started?'

TV ANCHOR

'Not just any old clock . . . the most accurate atomic clock in the world, and it's right here at the Institute of Technological Advancement and Research in downtown San Francisco. So don't do away . . .'

As the commercials start, the Doctor's face lights up.

DOCTOR

That must be a beryllium clock.

The doorbell rings. Grace grabs the remote and switches the TV off.

GRACE

They're here . . . thank God.

DOCTOR

Excellent! They can take us straight to the Institute.

Grace opens the door. The Master is standing there on the threshold wearing his shades. The Doctor comes face to face with him.

DOCTOR

We need to go straight to the Institute of Technological Advancement and Research. Do you know where that is?

The Master looks at Grace. She nods meaningfully.

MASTER
(smiling a tiny smile)

Of course I do . . .

FADE OUT

ACT FOUR

EXT. SAN FRANCISCO. NIGHT

Above the traffic and the lights, flashes of lightning fill the sky. Clouds race. A deep bass rumble fills the air.

INT. AMBULANCE. NIGHT

The highway lights are making wild patterns on the windscreen in front of Lee's face as he drives. There is no siren.

The Doctor, Grace and the Master are in the back. The Doctor is looking out of the back of the ambulance. He stares at the others, worried.

DOCTOR

What time is it?

GRACE
(trying to humour him)

It's just gone ten. Don't worry, I'm on the Board of Trustees at the Institute – they'll listen to me.

DOCTOR
(looking back out)

Can't this go any faster?

The Doctor is getting impatient. Grace looks at the Master and whispers:

GRACE

Can't you give him a sedative?

DOCTOR
(overlapping)

Why didn't you say you had access to a beryllium clock, Grace?

GRACE

I was more concerned about the Eye . . . of Destruction
. . .

DOCTOR

Of *Harmony*!

GRACE

(humouring him still)

Yes. And the fact that the planet will be sucked through
it at midnight. Face it — it's not often one has a Time
Lord in one's living room, Doctor . . .

*She looks pointedly at the Master, who smiles a tight smile
back at her.*

He likes me to call him 'Doctor' — Freud had a name for
it.

DOCTOR

Transference. *Ha!* Very witty, Grace, but I don't think so,
and *he* would have taken me seriously.

GRACE

Oh, he would have hung up his pipe if he'd met you.

DOCTOR

As a matter of fact, I *did* meet him.

GRACE

Of course, you're a Time Lord!

DOCTOR

And we got on very well.

GRACE

Did you know Madame Curie too?

DOCTOR

Intimately.

GRACE

Did she kiss as good as me?

MASTER
(interrupting)

Hey! Children . . .

They both look at the paramedic.

*The ambulance pulls to a sudden halt. The Master's shades
slip down his nose — Morphant eyes. Grace looks ahead. The
Master covers his eyes quickly, but the Doctor has seen.*

GRACE

Looks like a truck's blocking all the lanes.

DOCTOR

This planet is going to be destroyed and I'm stuck in a
traffic jam — Excuse me . . .

*Then the Doctor suddenly pulls the sunglasses off the Master,
whose reptilian eyes stare back.*

Get out, Grace. Get out now!

Grace looks at the Master's strange eyes.

GRACE

What's wrong with him?

DOCTOR

The Master!

Grace looks across to the Doctor. Could it all be true?

*The camera turns to the Master, who quickly rolls his head
back, filling his mouth with venom, and then suddenly gobs a
mouthful straight at us!*

*Grace puts up her arms to protect herself. He wrist is hit by
the venom and is immediately burnt. She screams.*

Meanwhile, the Doctor has kicked open the doors.

CLOSE–UP — GRACE'S WRIST

The Master's venom seeps deep into her, beneath the skin . . .

CLOSE–UP — GRACE

GRACE

Oh, God. *Oh, God! Get it off me! What is it?*

INT. AMBULANCE. NIGHT

The Doctor grabs a fire extinguisher and fires it straight at the Master, who screams out in pain.

Grace looks at the Doctor, terrified, as he turns back for her. He holds out his hand. She takes it. They run.

The Master is still screaming in agony, his face covered in gunk!

MASTER

I can't be injured like this! *Get this off me!*

Lee desperately wipes the white stuff off the Master's face. He's looking far worse for the wear . . .

EXT. HIGHWAY. NIGHT

A California Highway Patrol motorcycle heads out, travelling in the opposite direction to the traffic, to try and stop the Doctor and Grace.

The Doctor is running as fast as he can. Suddenly the motor-cycle patrolman pulls up in front of him.

PATROLMAN

Stop right here, sir . . . mam.

Grace homes to a halt beside the Doctor.

Go back to your vehicle.

The Doctor digs into one of his pockets. The patrolman instantly reaches for his gun. Grace suddenly puts herself in front of the Doctor.

GRACE

No. Stop! He's, er . . . he's *British!*

DOCTOR

Would you care for a Jelly Baby, officer?

80

PATROLMAN

A *what?*

The Doctor pulls the sweets from his pocket.

GRACE

Just take it —

She indicates that the Doctor is a little touched in the head. The patrolman takes one of the sweets and looks at it, then, seeing the Doctor's expectant look, he puts it in his mouth and starts to chew.

Then the Doctor reveals that he has sleight-of-handed the patrolman's gun into his possession. He points the gun at himself.

DOCTOR

Now stand back, or I'll shoot myself.

PATROLMAN

Don't be a fool.

DOCTOR

Are you with me, Grace?

Grace looks at him, completely torn.

GRACE

We don't stand a chance —

DOCTOR

I came back to life before your eyes . . . I held back death . . . I can't make your dream come true for ever, Grace, but I can make it come true today. What do you say?

GRACE

(after a beat)

Give me the gun . . .

The Doctor hesitates, then hands it to her. He doesn't know what she's going to do. The patrolman looks relieved, and goes to use his radio. Grace shoots out the radio! Pointing the gun

81

at the patrolmen, she says:
Give him the keys.
PATROLMAN
Now listen, pal. Life can deal you a bad hand sometimes, but this is no way —

EXT. HIGHWAY. THE TRAFFIC JAM. NIGHT
ALL THE NEARBY DRIVERS
Give him the keys!

EXT. HIGHWAY. NIGHT
The patrolman throws the keys to the Doctor, who smiles at Grace. She smiles back.

INT. AMBULANCE. NIGHT
The Master is recovering. Lee looks at him. The Master returns the gaze, his eyes streaming with pain . . .
MASTER
Well, what are you waiting for?
LEE
The road is blocked.
MASTER
This is an ambulance!
  Lee smiles.

LEE
Yeah!
  He guns the motor and turns on the siren.

EXT. HIGHWAY. NIGHT
The Doctor and Grace are starting the bike. Grace throws the gun away into a nearby field. They see the ambulance speeding up behind them.

GRACE

Maybe I should have kept the gun.

The Doctor takes off as fast as he can.

The patrolman is left spinning and then has to leap out of the way as the ambulance charges past.

Meanwhile, on the motorbike, Grace looks back nervously.

Doctor!

The Doctor looks in the wing mirror. He can see the ambulance gaining on them.

Look out!!

The Doctor looks up. Ahead, two huge lorries, side by side, are barrelling towards them, horns blaring.

DOCTOR

Breathe in, Grace!

They drive between the lorries, almost scraping the sides.

INT. AMBULANCE. NIGHT

Lee is driving. He looks across to the Master, who is obviously angry.

LEE

Don't worry!

MASTER

I'm not worried.

LEE

When I get all that gold, you know what I'm going to do?

MASTER

I don't want to know.

Lee laughs loudly at this, driving faster.

LEE
(still laughing)

You kill me . . .

MASTER

You want me to kill you?

LEE

No. I mean, you make me laugh, man.

MASTER

Well, I'm glad one of us is amused.

Lee stares at the Master.

LEE

Hey, cheer up. You'll get your body back soon and . . . and then we're a team, right?

MASTER

Yes, we're a team . . .

EXT. ROAD. NIGHT

The Doctor is driving as fast as he can, ignoring all the stop signs. He roars all the way to a junction, only narrowly avoiding being hit by cross-traffic.

GRACE

The Institute's down there! Take a right.

The Doctor swerves right. The ambulance is approaching the same junction, but it goes the other way.

INT. AMBULANCE. NIGHT

The Master looks in alarm at Lee.

MASTER

What are you *doing*, Lee!

LEE

This is a quicker way.

MASTER

It'd better be —

LEE

Look, I know these streets — this is my town! Trust me.

84

MASTER

Faster!

LEE

If we don't stop him, we're finished, both of us!

EXT. AMBULANCE. NIGHT
The ambulance is streaking by.

EXT. ROAD. NIGHT
The Doctor's bike is racing along at top speed, beside a railway line.

GRACE

I think we've lost them.

DOCTOR

Good. Hold tight.
Grace looks ahead and sees a water truck blocking the road.

GRACE

Not again!
The bike swerves sharply to the right and careers down the railway bank.

Grace holds on tight to the Doctor as they drive along the tracks, bumping up and down.
Doctor?

DOCTOR

What?

GRACE

I only have one life, can you remember that?

DOCTOR

I'll try.

GRACE

Great! I finally meet the right guy and he comes from another planet.

The bike flies back up the embankment and on to the road.

EXT. INSTITUTE OF TECHNOLOGICAL ADVANCEMENT AND
RESEARCH. NIGHT
*The bike skids to a halt and the Doctor and Grace look at what
lies before them. We are outside a brightly lit high-tech building.
The city lights are glowing around it and the bay is nearby.*

*A sign reads 'ITAR'. A banner reads '2000. The Beginning
of San Francisco Mean-Time!'*

*The camera pulls out to reveal that the building is ringed by a
heavy presence of security guards and police and media.*

GRACE

Oh, no! Look, Doctor.

And worse, the Master's ambulance is there already . . .

FADE OUT

ACT FIVE

INT. ITAR RECEPTION. NIGHT

The place is filled with guests. The Doctor and Grace are heading for the main desk. At the reception someone is checking names on a list.

GRACE

Dr Grace Holloway . . . and guest.

He finds her name, hands her a pass and smiles. As they walk inside, she hands the Doctor his security pass.

That's the first time being on the board of this place has ever really been of use to me.

DOCTOR
(looking around)

He must have found a back way in. I can't see him.

They approach a door that divides the reception area from the presentation area.

SECURITY MAN

Sorry, no one beyond this point.

GRACE

But this is Dr Bowman, from London. They're *waiting* for him.

She shows her pass. At the same moment the Doctor sees the Master and Lee beyond the door, heading towards the presentation room.

SECURITY MAN

You'll be allowed in with everyone else, sir.

INT. GLASS CORRIDOR. 2ND FLOOR. NIGHT

The Master and Lee speed around a corner and come face to face with four armed guards, all pointing their weapons straight at them.

INT. DINING AREA. NIGHT
The Doctor and Grace move through with the other people into the empty presentation area. The camera sweeps back and up to reveal a mass of media people and, above them, the beryllium clock, towering over the massive dining area . . .

Grace and the Doctor move through the tables, the Doctor looking up at the clock.

GRACE
(looking up at the clock also)
How are we going to get that on the back of a bike?

DOCTOR
We only need a tiny part of it.

GRACE
(whispered)
Make conversation — people are looking at us . . . So, time travel is possible?

DOCTOR
Anything is possible.

GRACE
And why don't you have the ability to transform your being *into* different beings, like, er . . .

DOCTOR
I do . . . But only when I die.

GRACE
And the other Time Lord? The Master?

DOCTOR
He's on his last life, fighting to survive, and as science has proved over and over, in the fight for survival there are no rules. Also, I'll let you in on a secret, Grace, as long as

you promise not to tell anyone . . .

Grace laughs as she catches the eye of a man who knows her, a certain Professor Wagg.

GRACE

Professor Wagg! I'm with Dr Bowman, from London . . . He has a secret he's going to share with us.

DOCTOR

Is there any chance of me getting a close look at the clock?

PROFESSOR WAGG

Oh, no! I'm afraid I'm the only person allowed up there.

DOCTOR

Well, maybe we could bend the rules a little . . .

PROFESSOR WAGG

Grace says you have a big secret . . . What is it?

The Doctor holds the Professor by the shoulder to emphasize the conspiratorial nature of his secret.

DOCTOR

I . . . am half human. On my mother's side.

There's a pause, then the Professor laughs too loudly.

PROFESSOR WAGG

Very witty!

He pulls away and moves on, leaving Grace looking into the Doctor's eyes. Her own eyes are shining and she smiles, believing him.

GRACE
(quietly)

Yes . . . I think you must be . . .

A beat . . . then the Doctor slowly lifts up his hand and reveals to Grace that he has sleight-of-handed Professor Wagg's security pass.

INT. CORNER ENTRANCE. 3RD FLOOR. NIGHT

The Doctor shows Professor Wagg's security pass to another guard.

> DOCTOR
> *(repeating Grace's line)*

Professor Wagg . . . and guest . . .

> *Grace smiles. The guard nods them through.*

> GRACE
> *(moving off)*

Thank you, Professor.

INT. BERYLLIUM CLOCK ON GLASS. NIGHT

The camera moves around the clock to reveal the Doctor and Grace kneeling at the back of it, quickly unscrewing the panel that holds the vital beryllium chip.

> DOCTOR
> *(whispered)*

Now this is when I wish I had my sonic screwdriver.

> *Little lights stop blinking as he works.*

> *We move in on a square of intricate micro-chips that sit at the heart of the complex machine. The Doctor is very carefully extracting the beryllium chip from the back of the clock. It's very small, only an inch or so.*

See, I told you it was small.

> GRACE

What is it they say . . .

> DOCTOR

Yes, they say that on my planet too.

> *The Doctor puts the chip into his palm and holds it tight. He and Grace stand up, only to discover that a young, zealous security guard, Gareth Fitzpatrick (eighteen), who may have seen what they were doing, is right beside them.*

Before Gareth can say anything, the Doctor points at him with the hand that is holding the chip.
I know you.

GARETH

You do?
The Doctor glances at his badge.

DOCTOR

Gareth, answer the second question on your mid-term exam, not the third. The third may look easier, but you'll mess it up.

GARETH

What?

DOCTOR

Remember! Answer the second question. Don't forget!

GARETH

I won't. Now can I see what's in your hand, sir . . .
The Doctor opens his hand and gives Gareth a Jelly Baby. The Doctor and Grace smile and move on.

As they walk away they are talking. They reach a balcony that looks down on all the floors below.

GRACE

What was that all about?

DOCTOR
(walking fast)

Gareth will head up the seismology unit of the UCLA task force ten years from now and devise a way of accurately predicting earthquakes.

GRACE
(amazed)

You mean it, don't you?

DOCTOR

Of course I do. His inventions ultimately save the human

race several times. *But* he has to graduate in poetry first.

GRACE

(looking down)

Hey, there's the kid that took your things.

We see Lee looking up at them from the second-floor crowds.

DOCTOR

(off-screen)

And look who's with him. Time to fly.

The Master sees the Doctor and gives chase.

The Doctor and Grace back away – fast.

INT. GLASS CORRIDOR. 2ND FLOOR. NIGHT

The Doctor and Grace race around the curving glass corridor, only to come face to face with the four guards who were trapping the Master. They have been slimed upright to the glass wall! Grace is horrified.

The Doctor, seeing a nearby alarm, sounds it. The whole building fills with noise.

GRACE

Why did you do that?

DOCTOR

Looked like things needed livening up. Grace, come on!

They race off, heading upwards.

INT. 2ND FLOOR. NIGHT

People are beginning to panic.

We cut to the stairwell, where Grace and the Doctor are racing up a ladder towards the roof as fast as they can.

Meanwhile, Professor Wagg is trying to calm people down.

PROFESSOR WAGG

Don't panic! Stay inside.

But he gets pushed over by the thronging crowd.

94

INT. STAIRWELL. NIGHT

The Master and Lee burst through into the stairwell, only to find the Doctor and Grace gone, and a fire hose unspooling.
 We move in on the Master, who is furious but thinking fast.

INT. RECEPTION AREA. NIGHT

As more security guards rush in, on the other side of a massive window behind them we can see the Doctor and Grace coming down the window on the fire hose.

EXT. THE FRONT OF ITAR. NIGHT

Grace and the Doctor make it to the ground.

GRACE

Just reached! You must have known exactly how long that fire hose was.

DOCTOR

Educated guess!
 They run to the patrol bike they left outside earlier, kick-start it and speed away.

EXT. ROAD. NIGHT

The Doctor is speeding along now.

GRACE

So do you know what's going to happen to me?

DOCTOR

You don't want to know.

GRACE

What!? You can't not tell me.

DOCTOR

Grace . . .

GRACE

Oh, God! Brian's going to move back in!

                          DOCTOR
I can't say.

                          GRACE
Please!

                          DOCTOR
The universe hangs by such a fragile thread of coinci-
dences, there is no point in trying to tamper with it
unless, like me, you are a Time Lord.

                          GRACE
OK, so just give me a few pointers.

   A siren sounds behind them. Grace looks back.

Oh, no . . . We're being followed!

EXT. ROSE ALLEY, CHINATOWN. NIGHT
The Doctor and Grace speed around the corner into the alley.
The camera moves back to reveal that they are being tracked
down by a motorbike patrolman, who is racing through other
streets to catch up with them. The Doctor sees the TARDIS.

                          DOCTOR
There she is!

                          GRACE
A police box?

   The Doctor tries the door. It's locked.

Now, *I* always leave a spare key . . .

                          DOCTOR
. . . in a secret compartment above the door?

                          GRACE
                        (smiles)
Yes! Great minds think alike.

                          DOCTOR
Up you go!

   He cups his hands for her to jump up. With his help, she is up and running her hand along the top of the Police Call Box sign.

There's a little cubbyhole just above the 'P'.

GRACE

Why a police box?

She finds it, clicks it open, takes out the key and jumps down. The Doctor unlocks the door. Grace sees behind them.

DOCTOR

Its cloaking device got stuck on a previous misadventure, but I like it like this.

GRACE

Doctor!

The motorbike patrolman swings into the alley at top speed. His headlight flares up over the TARDIS as he roars towards us. The Doctor kicks the doors to the TARDIS wide open.

The motorbike shoots inside! Grace covers her face, but there is no crash. The Doctor smiles mischievously.

Grace's jaw falls open as she hears the bike roaring back towards them from inside the small box. The motorbike shoots back out, carrying the traumatized patrolman!

Grace laughs, amazed.

Oh, my God . . .

The Doctor pulls Grace into the TARDIS and slams the door behind him. The patrolman can't get away from the scene fast enough.

INT. THE TARDIS, CONSOLE ROOM

Grace is looking around in amazement at the scale of the place. The Doctor dashes to the master control console and locks the door with the closing mechanism. Grace rubs her wrist where she was hit by the Master's venom. The colour of her skin is changing; a rash has spread over her whole arm. The cloister bell is tolling loudly from deep within. We close in on the Doctor, who is grim-faced.

DOCTOR

Hear that?

GRACE

Yes.

DOCTOR

It's a warning. The TARDIS is dying.

The time-rotor is still in the down position. The Doctor pulls a lever back. The screen still flashes 'Timing Malfunction'.

It's no good. We don't even have enough auxiliary power to move next door.

Grace looks on, worried, as the Doctor moves from instrument panel to instrument panel on the six-sided console. Finally he stops at one panel and opens it. He pulls something out and throws it on the floor.

The beryllium chip, Grace.

Grace gets the beryllium chip out of her pocket and hands it to the Doctor. He slides it into the panel. Then he attaches the new equipment with his fingers and screws and wires. They talk fast as he works.

GRACE

This looks pretty low-tech . . .

DOCTOR
(working)

It's a type–40 TARDIS. It can take me to any planet in the universe and to any date in that planet's existence. Temporal physics.

GRACE

You mean like interdimensional transference. That would explain the spatial displacement we went through as we passed over the threshold.

DOCTOR
(impressed)
If you like. That sounds good. There!
The screen stops flashing the malfunction warning . . .

INT. THE TARDIS, CLOISTER ROOM
The Eye starts to close.

INT. THE TARDIS, CONSOLE ROOM
The Doctor hangs his head back and breathes a sigh of relief.
DOCTOR
There . . . The Eye is closing. Now, let's see . . .
He looks at the read-out he's getting from the chronological navigation unit.
Come on!
He gives the console a thump. Then he looks really worried.
Oh, no . . .
Grace stares at where he's looking.
GRACE
What?

DOCTOR
I've got a horrible feeling we're already too late.
GRACE
(reading it)
11.48 – we've still got eleven minutes.
DOCTOR
Yes, but there's no context. Hold on . . .
He twiddles more dials and pulls more levers. A graphic representation of the entire universe on a holographic screen forms above the master control console. Grace is awed by its beauty, but the Doctor looks back to the chronological navigation unit.

INT. THE TARDIS, CLOISTER ROOM
The Eye closes . . . Darkness . . . An ominous low rumble continues.

INT. THE TARDIS, CONSOLE ROOM
The Doctor starts setting some slide controls.

GRACE

What are you doing?

DOCTOR

Setting coordinates for one minute after midnight.

GRACE

Why?

DOCTOR

If this is right, the Eye has already been open too long and there's no future. I just hope . . .
As he finishes, the universe above them swirls into a terrifying void.
Oh, no!

GRACE

Is . . . is this thing reliable?

DOCTOR

Whatever has started happening can't be stopped by shutting the Eye.

GRACE

How come you didn't know that?

DOCTOR

I've never opened the Eye before.

GRACE

Now you tell me!

DOCTOR

Just closing the Eye isn't enough, Grace. We have to go

back to before it was opened. Maybe even before we arrived.

GRACE

This is a time–machine.

DOCTOR

No power.

GRACE

What!?

DOCTOR

The Eye being open must have drained the TARDIS.

GRACE

Great!

DOCTOR

Sorry.

GRACE

You must have the power to get back. You must!

DOCTOR

Not enough.

GRACE

What about all your glorious predictions, all your knowledge of what is going to happen to Gareth, to me, to this city? That must come from somewhere. *Think!*

As she speaks, the Doctor formulates a plan, a very cunning one . . .

DOCTOR

Wait! Are you any good at setting alarm clocks?

GRACE

No.

DOCTOR

Good grief!

GRACE

But I'll *try*!

DOCTOR

Thank you. Now, listen very carefully . . .

As he speaks, the Doctor quickly pulls a tool box out of a secret compartment in the floor and puts it in front of Grace.

We pre-set the coordinates just as I divert the power from inside the Eye itself into the time-rotor here.

GRACE

So we jump-start the TARDIS?

DOCTOR

Sounds good.

He dips under the control console.

GRACE

So what do I do?

DOCTOR

Go over to the console where I replaced the beryllium chip and flip the top switch.

Grace moves over to the console. As she reaches out, she sees that her other hand has changed colour. We pan up to her face. All her skin has changed. She puts her hand to her forehead in pain.

Now pass me the neutron ram. Grace? . . . Grace?

Grace's eyes open. They have transformed into the eyes of the Master. Her hand reaches for the tools. The Doctor slides out from under the console.

Sorry, I'll show you which –

Before he can even look up, Grace smashes him over the head with the neutron ram. He collapses on the floor, unconscious.

We move back to reveal the Master and Lee emerging from the shadows. Grace looks at the Master. Her eyes have turned a shining black – pure evil . . .

FADE OUT

ACT SIX

INT. THE TARDIS, CLOISTER ROOM

The Doctor is coming around. He's tied to a stretcher on a gurney from the Master's ambulance. Grace and Lee look down on him as they push the gurney into the Cloister Room. The first thing the Doctor sees is the possessed face of Grace.

DOCTOR

Oh, no . . . Not you, Grace . . .

Grace looks at him. Her head tilts and there is a cold look in her dark eyes. The Doctor tries to move, but realizes he's been immobilized. He is wheeled past the now-closed Eye.

Really . . . this is no time to play doctors and nurses —

LEE

It's no good talking to her. She's possessed.

The Doctor looks at Lee.

DOCTOR

And you? You ran off with my things. Where are they?

LEE

They're not your things any more. Pretty soon everything round here's going to belong to the Master again.

DOCTOR

Again? What's he been telling you?

LEE

When he gets his body back from you, I'm going to be rich.

DOCTOR

And you believe him?

LEE

Things are weird enough already, why shouldn't I?

105

DOCTOR

I suppose he forgot to mention that there won't be any place left to spend your money.

Suddenly, and very coldly, Grace slaps the Doctor's face.

MASTER

(off-screen)

That's why we have no time to waste!

The Doctor's eyes swivel to the voice . . . The Master sweeps down the long stairs, now wearing magnificent robes that flow out behind him.

DOCTOR

But time to change —

MASTER

I always dress for the occasion.

DOCTOR

Well, I'm glad you're aware of the gravity of the situation.

MASTER

I never liked this planet, Doctor.

DOCTOR

Well, that's good, because it will cease to exist any minute now. What's the time?

MASTER

Time enough to get my body and get out of here . . . and take Lee with me.

Lee looks surprised.

The Master reaches the gurney and puts his decaying hand on the boy's shoulder.

Lee is the son I've always yearned for.

DOCTOR

Oh, please.

The Master picks up a horrific-looking surgical contraption.

MASTER

Grace, put it on him. I suspect you know how.
  Grace takes it.

DOCTOR

Lee . . . this is my TARDIS, this is my Eye and I am in
my *own* body.

MASTER

Don't listen to him.

DOCTOR

The Master has run out of all his lives and now he plans
to steal mine. *That's* the truth!

MASTER

Move him into position, Lee.
  *The Doctor is swivelled around by Lee so that his head is
  under Grace's hands.*

DOCTOR

Look at Grace. She is possessed by evil, not goodness.
  *But Grace's dark eyes just look at him as she lowers the con-
  traption towards his head. The Master smiles a tiny smile.*

MASTER

This won't hurt . . . much.
  Lee is watching, thinking . . .

INT. WALKER GENERAL HOSPITAL, PARTY ROOM. NIGHT
*A flip-over clock on the wall tells us it's 11.55. Party sounds
can be heard off-screen. An exhausted Salinger has just come
off duty. He enters the room to see the party in full swing.
Music blares. He smiles and wipes the sweat from his brow.
Curtis approaches from the party crowd, a drink for him in
her hand.*

CURTIS

Happy New Year.

SALINGER

I didn't think I'd make it in time.

CURTIS
(smiling)

Well, you did . . .

She kisses him.

Come on . . . Party!

INT. ITAR. NIGHT

Champagne is being poured into glasses.

Professor Wagg is taking the podium to start the clock. The buzz of the partying wealthy guests below him fills the air. He looks up to the clock proudly and whispers to himself.

PROFESSOR WAGG

. . . my life's work . . .

Then he crosses his fingers.

INT. THE TARDIS, CLOISTER ROOM

The Doctor has been chained upright on one of the balconies at the top of the stairs overlooking the Eye. The eye-opener is attached to his head and Grace is making the final adjustments to the straps that hold him in place.

Down below, the reflector staffs we saw earlier are being quickly moved into position by the Master and Lee.

DOCTOR

In 700 years no one has opened the Eye. How did you do it?

MASTER
(smiling)

Simple. Lee is human, you're only half! Now open the Eye, Lee, while I get in position.

He starts to move up the stairs.

INT. ITAR. NIGHT

A glass is being tapped! The cameras focus on the podium. Professor Wagg speaks into the hush, his voice echoing around the vast space.

PROFESSOR WAGG

Ladies and gentlemen, in three minutes the world will enter a new millennium, and with it a new standard of accuracy will come to how we measure time . . .

Gareth approaches and taps him on the shoulder, whispering something in his ear. The Professor's face goes beetroot.

What do you mean, 'It won't start'?

INT. THE TARDIS, CLOISTER ROOM

Lee pulls a reflector staff from its mound, as he did before. The Master is climbing the stairs.

DOCTOR

This is your last chance, Lee.

Lee looks up from what he's doing coolly.

LEE

This is my only chance.

MASTER
(to the Doctor)

Lee's right, Doctor. There is nothing for him here. No family, no gang, only death. But with me, he gets to see the universe.

DOCTOR

This is his last chance to stay alive and you know it.

MASTER
(losing his temper)

What do you know of last chances?

DOCTOR

More than you.

109

MASTER

I have wasted *all* my lives because of you, Doctor. Now I will be rid of you!

DOCTOR

'All' your lives? Didn't you tell Lee I had stolen your lives?

The Master realizes he has been caught out. Lee is looking at him. The Master moves back to him.

He lied to you, Lee. He has used all his lives, now he wants mine. Like I told you, this is *my* TARDIS and this is *my* body.

MASTER

Don't listen to him. Open the Eye, Lee.

Lee looks to the blank, possessed face of Grace.

Open the Eye!

Lee makes his choice.

LEE

No . . . You lied to me!

The Master flies back at Lee with all his remaining strength. He sends the boy spiralling into a stone pillar. His body collapses on the floor.

DOCTOR

How are you going to open the Eye now?

MASTER
(breathless)

Grace!

Grace turns towards him.

Come down here.

Grace moves down the stairs towards him.

DOCTOR

Unless I'm mistaken, in her present state of mind that won't work.

MASTER

Watch.

The Master slowly kisses her as if he were sucking the poison back out of her body. Her blank, black eyes give no response at first.

The Doctor looks on, helpless.

DOCTOR

No! Grace.

Then her eyes clear. The Master grips her head and she wakes, stunned. Her eyes return to normal, but before she can get her bearings, he thrusts her face into the beam.

Shut your eyes, Grace!

She screams at the light that is blinding her. She tries to pull back, but the Master holds her head there.

MASTER

Too late!

The Eye starts to open. The Master suddenly lets go and races up to his balcony.

GRACE
(reeling back)

I'm blind!

DOCTOR

Grace! Your sight will return.

But by the time her eyes adjust, the Master is in position and the first rays are starting to hit the reflectors, forming linking beams between the Doctor and the Master.

Grace starts to see what is happening.

MASTER
(as the first rays hit his face)

Ah, yes!

Grace has woken into a nightmare. With the blasting light, the Doctor can speak only in short bursts.

DOCTOR
(in terrible pain)

Grace!

GRACE

What's happening?

Grace sees the Master transfixed to the spot.

DOCTOR

He can't move . . . As long as the Eye links us . . . Remember, Grace.

GRACE
(remembering)

Re-route the power –

DOCTOR

In the Console Room. Go.

GRACE

But you'll die if I leave you!

DOCTOR

We'll all die if you don't!

We move in on the Doctor. The light from the reflectors is coming on to his face as the Eye opens even more.

Run, Grace!

She runs as fast as she can towards the Console Room.

CLOSE-UP – THE MASTER

Suddenly a rush of health comes through him. He is rooted to the spot.

MASTER

I can hear your thoughts, Doctor. I can feel your memories!

EXT. THE TARDIS

The TARDIS is changing. Its very surface is starting to glow.

EXT. SAN FRANCISCO. NIGHT
Boiling night clouds are moving, swirling, vortexing, ominously over the city. A major disaster of biblical proportions is about to hit.

INT. HOSPITAL PARTY ROOM. NIGHT
A small party is in full swing. Salinger stands up above the other doctors and calls out:

SALINGER

Thirty seconds!
  He holds up his watch. Everyone starts to count down. Pete, roaring through the party dressed as Richard Nixon, walks straight into a fancy-dress corpse and is scared to death.

INT. ITAR. NIGHT
The TV cameras are switched off. Everyone has loosened up and the party is really going with a swing. Gareth is being kissed by a girl. Professor Wagg is tapping his watch. It won't work.

PROFESSOR WAGG

Oh, what the hell? Twenty! Nineteen!

INT. THE TARDIS, CLOISTER ROOM
The Master is looking happier and happier. A warm glow continues to illuminate his face. His eyes have also returned to normal.

INT. HOSPITAL NIGHT
Everyone is screaming, hooters sound . . .

INT. ITAR. NIGHT
Champagne corks pop. Professor Wagg is now laughing uncontrollably.

PROFESSOR WAGG

Sixteen!

INT. THE TARDIS, CLOISTER ROOM
We are looking down on the Eye. It is now almost fully open.

MASSIVE CLOSE-UP — THE DOCTOR
The Doctor's eyes roll back in fear.

DOCTOR

This can't be how it ends . . . Stop this! *Please!*
Moving into his eye, shuddering, vibrating, the screen whites out . . .

FADE OUT

ACT SEVEN

INT. THE TARDIS, CONSOLE ROOM
The whole place is shuddering and swirling rings of light emanate from above the control console.

Grace is under the control console, feverishly trying to sort out the wiring. She is trying to attach different wires and hoping for the best each time.

GRACE

Oh, please, please God!

INT. THE TARDIS, CLOISTER ROOM
The reflected beams between the Master and the Doctor increase in intensity.

BIG CLOSE-UP — THE DOCTOR'S FACE
Shuddering . . .

BIG CLOSE-UP — THE MASTER'S FACE
Getting brighter . . .

EXT. ROSE ALLEY, CHINATOWN. NIGHT
Blue static effect dances all around the glowing TARDIS. The imminent danger that was in the sky is about to hit the earth!

INT. HOSPITAL. NIGHT
Everyone is singing 'Auld Lang Syne', arms linked. Suddenly the image distorts. The whole fabric of reality is being torn. All these people are suddenly twisted into a slow, blinding flash!

The numbers on the clock on the wall flip from 11.59 to

12.00. The blue static effect we saw in the alley is now engulf-ing the clock.

INT. THE TARDIS, CLOISTER ROOM
The Master now looks almost angelic, reborn in the wind and light.

MASTER

Alive. I'm alive!

INT. THE TARDIS, MASTER CONTROL CONSOLE
Grace connects two wires — the right wires. The finger of God! A massive spark. Streaks of power are seen streaming through the TARDIS. The lights all dip . . . then the console flares white hot. The time-rotor starts to move . . .

  Terrified, Grace's face comes up over the control console. The clock starts racing.

INT. THE TARDIS, CLOISTER ROOM
The light dips in the Eye.

DOCTOR

She did it . . . Your life-force is dying, Master!

MASTER

No!

EXT. ROSE ALLEY, CHINATOWN. NIGHT
The TARDIS starts to dematerialize, giving out the familiar, but this time massive, grinding sound. Before it totally disap-pears, we cut out of the scene, so that we are left hanging as to the fate of the planet . . .

INT. THE TARDIS, MASTER CONTROL CONSOLE
Grace is desperately trying to control the timing mechanism.

GRACE

Alarm clock, alarm clock, *think* alarm clock!

The screen flashes:

ENTERING TEMPORAL ORBIT . . .

Grace's eyes widen.

Temporal orbit! What is a temporal orbit?

EXT. INTERDIMENSIONAL VORTEX

The TARDIS is swirling through the same vortex that we saw in the title shot of the movie.

INT. THE TARDIS, CORRIDORS

The camera swirls as Grace is running like the wind through the TARDIS, back towards the Cloister Room.

INT. THE TARDIS, CLOISTER ROOM

The Doctor is almost dead when Grace races up the steps and on to his balcony. She puts her head between the beam and his face so they are face to face. She starts to free his eye-opener and his bonds.

The reflected beams between them broken now, the Master is free. He sees what is happening.

We turn back to Grace, freeing one of the arm straps.

GRACE

We're in a temporal orbit, Doctor. What is that? What *is* it?

DOCTOR

Grace!

Suddenly from nowhere, the Master grabs her and hurls her off the balcony, down on to the Eye!

The Doctor yells in primal rage at the Master and, summoning up all his remaining strength, breaks his bonds. He slams the Master back into the wall.

We cut to Grace, who is still barely alive.

Then cut back to the Doctor as he jumps the last couple of stairs and rushes to Grace's side.

GRACE!!!

It's too late . . . Grace is dead.

Then from nowhere again, we see that the Master has appeared with a reflector staff raised above his head and is bringing it smashing down on to the Doctor.

The Doctor manages to dodge the attack. The Master then back-hands him with the staff, knocking him off the Eye and down the stairs. The Master leaps on to the Doctor, picks him up and throws him back on to the Eye.

The Master then leaps back up on to the Eye, trying to land on the Doctor. Again the Doctor manages to avoid him.

You want dominion over the living, yet all you do is kill . . .

MASTER

Life is wasted on the living.

As the Master's temper builds, he begins to kick the Doctor and shove him aside. The Master is trying to pick up the Doctor, who manages to force him off the Eye with his hands.

In an instant the Master is preparing to leap back up at the Doctor, but this time the Doctor has managed to reach one of the staffs. As the incoming Master hurtles down on him, the Doctor manages to turn the staff, causing the mirror to focus its light on the face of the Master in flight, thereby causing him to be sucked into the Eye just as it is closing.

Just before the Eye closes for ever, the Doctor sees his mortal enemy spinning down deeper and deeper into the Eye. With an awesome burst of energy, the Master's body is ripped apart and explodes into a multidimensional cloud of particles. Then . . .

Only silence. The Eye has fully closed and things appear normal once more.

The Doctor is suddenly alone. For a while he doesn't move, but then he looks around him. He sees the bodies of Grace and Lee. He puts his head back and closes his eyes in pain.

INT. THE TARDIS, CONSOLE ROOM
The screen reads:

TEMPORAL ORBIT . . .

INT. THE TARDIS, CLOISTER ROOM
The Doctor is carrying Grace's body. He lays it down next to Lee and we can see that his heart is breaking.

Gradually the light from the Eye of Harmony fills the room. It gets warmer as the grinding of the TARDIS comes to a halt. The Doctor looks around him.

The navigational read-out tells us that it's December 29th.

The Doctor looks back to his friends. Their bodies seem to glow as the light becomes warmer and warmer. Suddenly they are breathing . . .

A slow smile of relief crosses the Doctor's face. Lee is the first to open his eyes. He sees the Doctor.

LEE

Doctor . . . I have your things.

The Doctor grins. Then Grace opens her eyes. He looks at her.

DOCTOR
(softly)

Hello, Grace . . . How does it feel to hold back death?

She smiles at him . . . then hugs him. As if in response, the Eye of Harmony closes. The lights return to normal. The Doctor sees this and pulls away.

Incredible! Did you see that? What a sentimental old

thing this TARDIS is.

He turns back to them. They are smiling at him.

Well, you have both been somewhere I have never been
. . . Congratulations.

GRACE
(quietly)

It's nothing to be scared of, Doctor.

DOCTOR
(after a beat)

That's good to hear.

GRACE

Did we go back far enough?

DOCTOR
(eyes twinkling)

Must have done, or I'm talking to a couple of ghosts . . .
And I don't believe in ghosts.

INT. THE TARDIS, CONSOLE ROOM

*The Doctor is throwing switches and turning dials. The
TARDIS reacts as they talk.*

LEE

Where's the Master?

Strange noises sound from above . . .

DOCTOR

Mmmm . . . indigestion. Let's just say his plan backfired
on him . . . Now, let's see where we are.

*Suddenly the holographic representation of the universe flashes
up over us . . .*

There . . . the future. And look over there on the other
side of your galaxy . . . that's home.

GRACE

Gallifrey.

> DOCTOR

250 million light years – ten minutes from here in this old thing.

> GRACE

So where are we?

> DOCTOR

December 29th. You want to get off here?

> GRACE

Don't think I could live through all that again.

> LEE

I *definitely* wouldn't live through it.

> DOCTOR

Well, that's reason enough for me.

INT. HOSPITAL. NIGHT
A small party is in full swing. Salinger stands up above the other doctors and calls out:

> SALINGER

Thirty seconds!
He holds up his watch. Everyone starts to count down. We see the faces of Curtis and Wheeler. Pete is roaring through the party dressed as Richard Nixon. Only twenty seconds left.

INT. ITAR. NIGHT
Gareth is kissing a girl. Professor Wagg is tapping his watch. It won't work.

> PROFESSOR WAGG

Oh, what the hell? Twenty! Nineteen!

EXT. PARK BY THE BAY. NIGHT
The TARDIS slowly materializes out of thin air. This time no one sees it.

The Doctor, Grace and Lee come out of the TARDIS just in time to hear the cheers go up all over the city, and see fireworks explode over the bay. We pan along their faces as they look up high into the sky . . .

Watching the fireworks, Lee and Grace are spellbound. Singing fills the air: 'Should auld acquaintance be forgot' etc.

DOCTOR

Good . . . That is as it should be.

The Doctor looks to where his timepiece should be, then at Lee.

LEE

Your things . . .

Lee gives him his things back: first the timepiece, then the screwdriver and the key.

Oh, and these too . . .

He hands the Doctor the two bags of gold.

DOCTOR

Keep them. Next Christmas, take a big vacation . . . just don't be here.

GRACE

There you go. Interfering again.

DOCTOR

Oh, and Grace –

GRACE

Don't!

DOCTOR

Why not?

GRACE

I know who I am . . . That's enough.

LEE

You mean I can really keep these?

DOCTOR

Sure.

124

LEE

Then I'm getting out of here before you change your mind.

DOCTOR

Bye, Lee.

They watch him go. The Doctor then turns to Grace.

I was serious . . . Do you want to come with me?

GRACE

Do you want to come with me?

A beat . . .

DOCTOR

I'm tempted.

The singing of 'Auld Lang Syne' drifts on the night air. Grace smiles . . .

GRACE

I'll miss you.

DOCTOR

Not me. I'm easy to find. I'm the guy with two hearts.

GRACE

I didn't mean that.

DOCTOR

I know.

They kiss. Fireworks fill the air.

GRACE

Thank you, Doctor.

DOCTOR

Thank *you*, Doctor!

Grace watches as the Doctor heads back into the TARDIS. He closes the door . . . A beat . . . The familiar grinding sound. It disappears.

INT. THE TARDIS

The Doctor feels the controls. He pulls levers, turns dials, punches in numbers and then hopes for the best. He smiles.

DOCTOR

That sounds better . . . Now, where shall we go?

As if in reply, the time-rotor lights glow brighter and brighter and we're off! We close in on the Doctor's face, alive again, and wait with baited breath . . . The famous music fills the air and the Doctor's next adventure is about to begin.

FADE OUT

DOCTOR WHO

The Novel of the Film

Gary Russell

Late December, 1999: the brink of a new millennium. San Francisco is preparing for a new era. But things are not looking good. There are two time-travellers in San Francisco, and only one of them is the Doctor . . .

The novel of the film is priced £3.99 and is available from all good bookshops.

ISBN 0 563 30800 4

A video of the film is now available from BBC Video, priced £14.99.

BBCV 5882